For Conor and Sadhbh
ED and JG

For Kate Janaki (Ella) and Dara Luca
SK

Conor - the facts

The name Conor, more common as Connor in Britain, is derived from the legendary figure, Conchobar Mac Nessa, meaning wolf lover or lover of hounds. One of the most detailed characters in Celtic mythology, he was subject to variations in interpretation throughout the ages. The name may be linked to the Breton title, Conan, borne by early royal figures in Brittany.

Conor was King of Ulster at the time of the Red Branch Knights and Cuchulainn. In pre-tales to *The Cattle Raid of Cooley*, his accession as king while still a youth, through his mother's deception, is explained. She convinces his half brother, King Fergus, to allow the still youthful Conor to reign for a year.

During this time his mother ensures that he distributes wealth among the population, behaves justly and wisely on all matters and feasts the nobles to keep them on his side. He quickly earned a reputation as a just and generous ruler. So successful was this strategy that when his year was up the people insisted on keeping Conor as King.

Once confirmed on the throne he quickly became cruel and treacherous, driving Fergus to Connaught. He doubled the size of his army and attempted to take over the rest of the country. Conor's only weakness was when a periodic magical sickness - inflicted, in some versions, by the goddess, Macha, whom he insulted - overcame the king and the Red Branch Knights.

One of his innovations, which inspired our story, was a special school for young people, where every form of sport and physical fitness training was provided. This echoed the version of his own youth as son of the druid, Cathbad. The underlying intention, however, was the creation of a new corps for the legendary Red Branch Knights.

Conor is a background figure in the early stories of Cuchulainn. He features significantly in the epic tale, *The Cattle Raid of Cooley (Tain Bo Cuillnge)* towards the end of which he is almost slain by the deposed Fergus. His treachery is described in detail in *The Fate of the Sons of Usnach*, the so-called third sorrow of story telling in Celtic mythology.

Various versions of his birth and parentage exist, principally that his father was the giant king, Fachtna Fathach, or the druid, Cathbad. His death is variously described as occurring in battle or, in later Christian versions, on Good Friday. Some analysts of the Conor saga assert it is the basis for the King Arthur tales, which emerged firstly in Wales and, during the Middle Ages, throughout Britain.

Once there was a boy called Conor. He loved to play. He played taxi-driver with his cars. He stacked his building bricks high to make bridges and monsters. He led his soldiers into the garden, but he never led them back again. Late every evening his mum or dad would go searching for them.

Conor's favourite game was King of the Castle. When he got the chance he put on his dad's dressing gown and became a king dressed in fine robes. The armchair where his mum sat to read a magazine was his throne. His toy soldiers were his loyal subjects.

Once he led his soldiers into the garden in the rain wearing his dad's dressing gown. He really got into trouble that day!

Conor imagined that he was the wisest king that ever lived. All the people in the land were happy because he was so generous. His soldiers were pleased because they never had to go to battle. The deer in the forest were content because nobody hunted them. Brightly coloured flowers bloomed because King Conor said that there should be plants at the side of every road.

In Conor's kingdom the children were happiest of all. They spent their days playing sport of every kind. Swimming and running, chasing and hiding, football and hurling, tennis and cricket, skipping and jumping.

The children were even happier because they never had to change their clothes or shoes or socks after playing. They did wash and dry their hands carefully though!

13

Many years later, when Conor was bigger, he became a real king. Now he had to do important things, like ride a horse while wearing a heavy crown on his head all day. Sometimes he had to travel in a carriage, when he wanted to stay home and watch television. He visited kings in far away countries and ate big meals with lots of strange vegetables that tasted yuk. On his birthday he had to go on a big parade, and he never got to eat his special chocolate cake with cream. Poor King Conor was miserable.

Then one day he noticed that he was not the only one who was unhappy.

His soldiers worried about going to war. The deer were hunted by strangers. The flowers were trampled by horses and soldiers on the road each day. The people worried that the king no longer cared for them.

Worst of all the children were miserable. They stayed inside because there was nowhere safe to play.

Conor was so busy doing important things that he had forgotten about everyone else.

Then he remembered all the fun he had when he was young. "I must make the children in my kingdom happy again," he said.

He rubbed his chin and wondered about what he should do.

He walked up the stairs thinking. He walked down the stairs thinking. He did so much thinking that he rubbed half the beard off his chin.

It was then that Conor learned that no matter how busy or important we are, we must not forget the things that are important to other people.

Soon he issued a royal command. "Every child in my kingdom shall be invited to a special summer camp with their friends. They can play football and hurling, tennis and cricket, hockey and swimming, just like I did when I was young. I'll make sure they all get fruit juice to drink as well," he said.

From that day to this his royal command is obeyed in every city and town in the land. People everywhere run summer camps with just one instruction from King Conor: 'Make sure that all the children can play and laugh and be happy.'

Perhaps you'll go on a summer camp one day soon. Watch out for King Conor. Oh! and don't forget to drink your fruit juice!

What's in a name?

Usually centuries of history, religious or legendary tradition.

The main source of names is in religious history, in the names of saints (Catherine) and, post Reformation, in the *Bible* and *Old Testament* in particular (Sarah and Adam). The *Koran* provides additional perspective on many of these names.

Names from Celtic legend, like Conor, have recently gained increased attention internationally.

Another source is classical, from pagan, royal or literary figures, e.g. Lawrence (Latin) and Chloe (Greek literature). Historical figures, such as Victoria, also provide a rich source.

Then there's Jack! It probably deserves a category all of its own having appeared from nowhere - but perhaps from Jankin, a version of John - to become the ubiquitous name in fairy tales and now a highly popular first name.

Recently parents have become much more adventurous. This follows the decrease in family and religious bonds that resulted in names passing from generation to generation. Increased access to other cultures has led to 'name globalisation', with names like Tanya, Brooklyn and Chelsea now more popular.

Other names recall a particular individual or event. The *Bible* and *Koran* name, Aron, received a new lease of life - and spelling - from Elvis Aaron Presley. Jack